To little
sisters
everywhere

ONE BIG HAPPY

SHOULD I SPIT ON HIM?!

Rick Detorie

NANTIER · BEALL · MINOUSTCHINE
Publishing inc.
new york

Also Available:
Son of Drabble by Kevin Fagan, $9.95 (plus $3 P&H)

NBM has over 150 graphic novels available
Please write for a free color catalog to:
NBM -Dept. S
185 Madison Ave. Ste. 1504
New York, N.Y. 10016

ISBN 1-56163-172-8

Printed in Canada

Ruthie's LIST OF **DON'TS** FOR BIG BROTHERS

ALSO **DON'T** HIT PINCH BITE TRIP SMACK or ANNOY your sister in any way!

7

I CAN'T GET USED TO DRIVING AN AUTOMATIC! YOU KNOW **ME**, I LOVE THE FEEL OF A STICK SHIFT!

WHEN I HAD THIS TOOTH PULLED THEY WANTED TO KNOCK ME OUT, BUT I WOULDN'T LET 'EM! YOU KNOW **ME**!

DID YOU TRY THE TOMATO SURPRISE? I DIDN'T! YOU KNOW **ME**, I CAN'T ABIDE THE STUFF!

IT'S ALL RIGGED! THAT'S WHY YOU'LL NEVER CATCH ME BUYING LOTTERY TICKETS. YOU KNOW ME!

YOU SHOULD GET YOURSELF ONE OF THOSE VIBRATING RECLINERS. YOU'LL LOVE IT! TRUST ME. YOU KNOW ME!

YOU WON'T CATCH ME ACCEPTING A SENIOR CITIZEN DISCOUNT! I'M NOT OLD, AND I HAVE TOO MUCH PRIDE!

YOU KNOW **ME**! EXCUSE ME, MAY I ASK YOU A QUESTION?

SURE, GO AHEAD.

WHO **ARE** YOU?

ELLEN'S THE GUEST SPEAKER TODAY IN JOE'S CLASS.

SHE'S TALKING ABOUT HER CERAMICS BUSINESS.

HOW NICE!

YOU KNOW, KIDS **LOVE** ART! I BET THEY'RE ASKING HER A MILLION QUESTIONS ABOUT THE HOWS AND WHYS OF THE CREATIVE PROCESS!

WHAT KIND OF MONEY ARE WE TALKING HERE?

YEAH, WHAT DO YOU MAKE AFTER TAXES?

EXCUSE ME, IS THIS THE PLACE WHERE YOU GIVE A FREE DESSERT TO KIDS ON THEIR BIRTHDAY?

WHY, YES!

OH, GOODY! WHAT WOULD YOU SAY IF I TOLD YOU THAT TODAY IS **MY** BIRTHDAY?

I'D SAY, **TERRIFIC!** HOW OLD ARE YOU?

SIX AND-A-HALF.

GRANDMA, GRANDPA CALLS WAITRESSES "HONEY"!

HE CALLS THE GROCERY CHECKER "SWEETHEART," AND THE CAFETERIA LADY "DARLIN'."

OH, THAT DOESN'T BOTHER ME, RUTHIE!

BUT WHAT SPECIAL NAME IS LEFT FOR **YOU**?!

"CO-SIGNER."

HELLO, YOU'VE REACHED ROSE AND NICK'S VOICE MAIL.

IF YOU'RE ONE OF OUR KIDS LOOKING TO BORROW MONEY, PRESS "ONE" AND HANG UP. IF YOU'RE A RELATIVE CALLING TO SHARE YOUR PROBLEMS WITH US, PRESS "TWO" AND HANG UP.

IF YOU'RE A SALESPERSON, PRESS "THREE" AND HANG UP. IF YOU'RE ANYBODY ELSE CALLING WITH TASTY TRASHY GOSSIP, SPEAK WHEN YOU HEAR THE BEEP.

BEEP.

I'M TIRED OF GOING THERE!

IT'S MOUNTAINOUS!

MONOTONOUS.

AND THE FOOD STINKS!

THE SEATS ARE UNCOMFORTABLE, AND THE HIRED HELP IS BOSSY AND CRABBY! SO WHY, MOM, **WHY**?!

BECAUSE, RUTHIE, IT'S SCHOOL AND YOU **MUST** GO.

OKAY, BUT I'LL BRING HOME GERMS!

COOKIE SCHVENGLE BROUGHT AN X-RAY OF HER DAD'S BROKEN TOE TO SHOW 'N' TELL TODAY!

MY SHOW 'N' TELLS ARE **NEVER** THAT INTERESTING! NOBODY AROUND HERE EVER BREAKS ANY BONES!

GEE, RUTHIE, WOULD YOU LIKE ME TO BREAK ONE OF MY FINGERS TO IMPRESS YOUR CLASS?

OF COURSE NOT, DADDY!

I'D NEED A MUCH **BIGGER** BONE, LIKE AN ARM OR A LEG!

STOP IT, BOTH OF YOU!

COME HERE, I WANT TO TELL YOU TWO A TRUE STORY!

MANY YEARS AGO, MY MOTHER CAME TO THIS COUNTRY AS A CHILD ON A BIG SHIP.

THE DAY BEFORE THE SHIP DOCKED AT ELLIS ISLAND, MY MOM AND HER BROTHER JIM HAD A TERRIBLE FIGHT...

A STUPID, **SENSELESS** FIGHT.

MY MOTHER LAY AWAKE THAT NIGHT CRYING.

BOO HOO, SOB!

THE NEXT DAY, AS THE FAMILY DISEMBARKED, THEY WERE STOPPED BY AN IMMIGRATION OFFICIAL.

THIS CHILD'S EYES ARE RED AND SWOLLEN! SHE MAY BE **DISEASED!**

AND THE WHOLE FAMILY WAS ALMOST DENIED ENTRY!

WHAT VALUABLE LESSON CAN WE LEARN FROM THIS STORY?

IMMIGRATION OFFICIALS ARE SCUM!

HEY! HE SHOVED ME AGAIN!

One Big Happy

LISTEN UP, AND LISTEN GOOD!

WHEN RUTHIE WAS IN NURSERY SCHOOL, THE "EXPERT" SAID:

SHE'S ACADEMICALLY IMMATURE.

AND YOUR MOTHER SAID:

SHE'S **FOUR**, FOR CRYING OUT LOUD!

WHEN JOE WAS IN KINDERGARTEN, THE "EXPERT" SAID:

HE HAS A PROBLEM WITH INTERGENDER SOCIAL INTERACTION.

AND YOUR MOTHER SAID:

HE DOESN'T LIKE GIRLS!

IN FIRST GRADE, THE "EXPERT" SAID ABOUT RUTHIE:

SHE EXHIBITS INAPPROPRIATELY CONTROLLING BEHAVIOR IN GROUP SETTINGS.

AND YOUR MOTHER SAID:

SHE'S BOSSY!

WHEN JOE WAS IN SECOND GRADE, THE "EXPERT" SAID:

beleif
crane
money
soohte

HE SOMETIMES TRANSPOSES LETTERS. HE MAY BE SLIGHTLY DYSLEXIC.

AND YOUR MOTHER SAID:

HE'S A LOUSY SPELLER!

SUGGESTION:

USE THE MONEY YOU WOULD'VE SPENT ON THE "EXPERTS" TO BUY YOUR MOTHER A WASHING MACHINE. SHE NEEDS A NEW ONE, AND IT WOULDN'T KILL YOU.

HEY! WHO LET MY MOTHER USE MY COMPUTER AGAIN?

WELCOME TO THE SHOW! TELL US ABOUT YOUR...

FORGET IT! HERE COMES A REAL GUEST!
SWOOSH
RUTHIE'S TEA TIME

HELLO, GORGEOUS!
HI, GRANDPA! WELCOME TO MY TALK SHOW!
RUTHIE'S TEA TIME TALK SHOW

I DON'T KNOW WHAT TO TALK ABOUT!
TALK ABOUT WHAT PEOPLE TALK ABOUT ON TALK SHOWS!

OH!

IT'S MY PARENTS' FAULT THAT I'M NOT HAPPY!
RUTHIE'S TEA

IT'S SOCIETY'S FAULT I'M OVERWEIGHT! IT'S THE GOVERNMENT'S FAULT I'M NOT RICH!

IT'S ORGANIZED RELIGION'S FAULT THAT I FEEL SO GUILTY! IT'S THE MASS MEDIA'S FAULT THAT I'M CONFUSED!

I BLAME EVERYONE FOR EVERYTHING!

I HAVE, HOWEVER, JOINED SEVERAL SELF-HELP GROUPS, INCLUDING WHINERS ANONYMOUS AND ADULT CHILDREN OF ADULT CHILDREN.
RUTHIE'S TEA TIME TALK SHOW

I'M FINE, EXCEPT THE SEARCH FOR CONTROL OF MY LIFE IS CONTROLLING MY LIFE!

STOP IT! YOU'RE CONFUSING THE CHILD!
THEN THERE'S MY WIFE...
TISSUE?
RUTHIE'S TEA TIM

20

HELP, MOM! BUGGY'S ON THE PHONE CALLING ME "BABE" AND "GIRLFRIEND"!

I'LL HANDLE IT, RUTHIE!

I'VE HAD IT WITH THIS PINT-SIZED MAKE OUT ARTIST!

HELLO, BUGGY? THIS IS RUTHIE'S MOM... YEAH... WHAT? OH, A SWEAT SHIRT, SLACKS, UH...

WHAT DO YOU MEAN, **WHAT AM I WEARING**?!

MAY I HELP YOU WITH SOMETHING?

I'M LOOKING FOR A VALENTINE CARD FOR A BOY NAMED BUGGY.

HE KEEPS TELLING EVERYBODY I'M HIS GIRLFRIEND, BUT I'M NOT!

WHAT KIND OF MESSAGE ARE YOU LOOKING FOR?

OH, SOMETHING LIKE: *ROSES ARE RED, VIOLETS ARE BLUE. IF YOU DON'T KNOCK IT OFF, I'LL PULVERIZE YOU!*

I DON'T THINK WE HAVE ANY CARDS CONTAINING CHEERY **THREATS**!

OH, IT DOESN'T HAVE TO BE **CHEERY**.

LOOK, GRANDPA, A BUNNY! HE MUST'VE AWAKENED EARLY FROM HIBERNATION!

SOMETIMES, RUTHIE, WHEN I HEAR THE SOPHISTICATED, GROWN-UP WAY YOU SPEAK...

I FORGET THAT YOU'RE STILL A CHILD!

SHHHH...

IF WE'RE VERY, VERY QUIET, MAYBE HE'LL TALK TO US!

AND OTHER TIMES...

ONE BIG HAPPY

GEE, TIKI, I HOPE THE WIND DOESN'T MUSS MY HAIR!

NO CHANCE OF THAT HAPPENING, HAL!

SO, WATCH OUT... IT'S GOING TO BE WINDY OUT THERE TONIGHT!

HAH, HAH, HAH, HAH, HAH!

HAH, HAH, HAH! AREN'T WE WITTY?!

DAD, WHY ARE YOU MAKING US WATCH THE NEWS TONIGHT?

YEAH, IT'S BORING!

JUST WAIT! IT'S ALMOST OVER.

BACK TO YOU, TIKI...

THANKS, HAL, AND WE END OUR BROADCAST TONIGHT WITH VALENTINE MESSAGES FROM SOME OF YOU FOLKS OUT THERE!

WITH TIKI

HI, JUDY! I LOVE YOU AND BABY KIRBY AND, SEE, I REMEMBERED TO BUY KITTY LITTER!

KITTY Litter

HAPPY VALENTINE'S DAY TO BERT, THE LOVE OF MY LIFE, AND ALSO TO EDDIE, MY HUSBAND.

LISA HERE HAS, LIKE, A MAJOR THING FOR THIS GUY NAMED TED!

EEEEEE! OH, STOP!

I LOVE MYSELF, BECAUSE ONLY AFTER YOU LEARN TO LOVE YOURSELF WILL SOMEONE ELSE FIND YOU LOVABLE. HAPPY VALENTINE'S DAY TO ME.

ROSES ARE RED, VIOLETS ARE BLUE, TIKI, TIKI, TIKI, WAH-WAH-WOO!

HAPPY VALENTINE'S DAY TO MY WIFE ELLEN AND OUR KIDS JOE AND RUTHIE! I LOVE YOU ALL!

HOW SWEET, FRANK!

WELL, WHAT DO YOU THINK, GUYS?

WHOSE DOG WAS THAT BEHIND YOU?!

YEAH, IT WAS CUTE! SUCH A CUTE LITTLE DOG!

GRANDPA, I HAVE A PROBLEM WITH TIME.

WELCOME TO THE CLUB, RUTHIE.

TIME SNEAKS UP ON YOU! YOU WAKE UP ONE DAY AND FIND YOU'RE OLD!

AND YOU SEEM TO BE **OLD** A LOT LONGER THAN YOU WERE **YOUNG**. YEAH, TIME SURE IS TRICKY!

MY PROBLEM IS MORE LIKE, WHAT IS IT WHEN THE BIG HAND IS ON THE FIVE AND THE LITTLE HAND IS ON THE ONE?

JOE, WHAT'S ALL THIS NOISE UP HERE?

I WAS...

YOU WERE SUPPOSED TO BE ASLEEP AN HOUR AGO. NOW GO TO BED!

BUT...

BUT, NOTHING! SHHH... YOU'LL WAKE RUTHIE.

YEAH, RIGHT!

WHY ARE BOYS SO DIFFICULT AT THIS AGE?

WHICH ONE SHOULD WE DO THIS TIME, RUTHIE?

HMMM...

I KNOW! A KILLER SHARK!

YEAH, A GIANT SHARK WHO POPS OUT OF THE BATHTUB AND SWALLOWS THE MEAN BIG BROTHER WHO SHOOTS RUBBER BANDS AT HIS POOR LITTLE SISTER!

WE'RE TALKING ABOUT A GELATIN MOLD, DEAR.

OKAY, THE STAR.

ROY, DO YOU KNOW THAT YOUR CHRISTMAS LIGHTS ARE STILL UP?!

OH...SO THEY ARE!

DON'T YOU THINK IT'S ABOUT TIME YOU REMOVED THEM? PEOPLE ARE STARTING TO TALK!

YEAH, **WHO**?! WHO'S TALKING?

ME!

THAT GUY AHEAD OF US JUST SPIT OUT HIS CAR WINDOW!

UGH!

WE JUST RAN OVER IT! I'M TOTALLY GROSSED OUT! YOU MIGHT AS WELL TURN THE CAR AROUND, DAD!

SCHOOL IS OUT OF THE QUESTION TODAY!

NICE TRY, RUTHIE.

THERE'S MELISSA. SHE THINKS SHE'S SO SPECIAL!

SHE GETS STRAIGHT A'S AND OUR TEACHER MISS CHOWDER BRAGS ABOUT HER!

MISS CHOWDER EVEN TOLD US THAT MELISSA WAS OVER ED CHEEVER!

ED CHEEVER?!

DO YOU MEAN AN OVERACHIEVER?

WHOEVER ED CHEEVER IS!

GUESS WHAT, RUTHIE?! I'M GOING ON *THE MISS DEBBIE SHOW!*

THE TV SHOW?

OH, BIG **DEAL**, JAMES! THAT DUMB OLD SHOW? **PSHEEEW!!!**

YOU COULDN'T **PAY** ME TO GO ON THAT SILLY LITTLE KIDS' SHOW!

MOM, I WANNA GO ON *THE MISS DEBBIE SHOW!*

THE MISS DEBBIE SHOW IS STILL ON THE AIR?!

YEP, AND I WANNA GO ON IT!

IT'S THE SAME MISS DEBBIE I USED TO WATCH THIRTY YEARS AGO! WHOA...SHE LOOKS BAD!

I CAN TOP THAT! I REMEMBER HER **RADIO** SHOW BACK IN THE 1940s!

WHOA... SHE LOOKS **GOOD!**

MY NAME IS RUTHIE AND I'M IN THE FIRST GRADE, BUT I COULD READ WHEN I WAS FOUR YEARS OLD!

I HAVE A BROTHER AND A MOM AND DAD AND WE LIVE NEXT DOOR TO MY GRANDMA AND GRANDPA.

I WALK MRS. VAETH'S DOG, ROWDY, AND I GET A QUARTER EACH TIME I DO; AND MY GRANDPA SOMETIMES GIVES ME A WHOLE DOLLAR FOR ABSOLUTELY NOTHING!

FINE, DEAR, NOW LET'S HEAR SOME OF THE OTHER CHILDREN'S INTRODUCTIONS!

DON'T YOU WANT TO HEAR ABOUT MY AUNT DELIA'S CYST?

I DO!

THE MISS DEBBIE SHOW

RUTHIE, DO YOU HAVE TO PRESS YOUR FACE SO CLOSE TO THE PAPER?

RUTHIE?

z

THE 🌐 🪗 2

COMPLETE THESE PHRASES:
YOU CAN LEAD A HORSE TO WATER, BUT YOU CAN'T teach him to type.

NOTHING SUCCEEDS LIKE a weed.

PEOPLE WHO LIVE IN GLASS HOUSES should always wear something.

IT IS BETTER TO HAVE LOVED AND LOST THAN to get your finger stuck in a door.

BIRDS OF A FEATHER are practically naked.

A PENNY SAVED Isn't worth a dime.

PLINK

WE HAVE NOTHING TO FEAR BUT the furnace.

BARUMMP

ONE BIG HAPPY

OH! I KNOW! I KNOW!

JOE, LET'S PLAY FORTS!

OKAY, RUTHIE, BUT I GET TO BE JOHN WAYNE, AND THE COUCH IS MY FORT!

OKAY, BUT I'M ROBIN HOOD AND I CAN FLY AND THE WHOLE DINING ROOM IS MY FOREST!

OKAY, BUT THIS DOG IS MY FRIEND CAPTAIN KIRK AND THE WHOLE ENTIRE UPSTAIRS IS THE STARSHIP ENTERPRISE.

FINE, BUT MALIBU BARBIE HAS SUPER POWERS AND IS TOTALLY INVINCIBLE!

OKAY, BUT MY FORT HAS A PROTECTIVE SHIELD, AND THE PILLOWS ARE NUCLEAR WARHEADS!

OKAY, BUT THIS ROBOT IS ON MY SIDE AND HE'S THE BAD TERMINATOR AND CAN BECOME ANYTHING!

WELL, UM...

HEY, WHAT DID YOU TWO DECIDE TO PLAY?

NOTHING.

YEAH, WE WENT WAY OVER BUDGET!

RUTHIE, TAKE MY HAND, PLEASE!

OH, MOM, I'M TOO OLD FOR THAT **BABY** STUFF!

HIGH AND OUTSIDE...
✳ CLICK ✳
A PSYCHOTIC CHIROPRACTOR...
✳ CLICK ✳
STATIC CLING...
✳ CLICK ✳

UFOs HAVE LANDED...
✳ CLICK ✳
I'M PRACTICALLY INNOCENT...
✳ CLICK ✳
SHE'S WALKING!
✳ CLICK ✳

NO STINKIN' BADGES...
✳ CLICK ✳
MIDEAST PEACE PLAN...
✳ CLICK ✳
THE WEED WHACKER KILLER...
✳ CLICK ✳

WIVES DRIVEN INSANE BY HUSBANDS WHO KEEP SWITCHING CHANNELS—NEXT ON *OPRAH!*

THAT ONE! THAT ONE!

KIDS SURE GET BOSSED AROUND A LOT!

DON'T DO THIS! DON'T DO THAT! DON'T LEAVE THE DOOR OPEN! DON'T PUT THAT IN YOUR MOUTH! DON'T TOUCH! DON'T RUN!

JEEZE, WHEN DOES IT END?!

DAD, DON'T LIFT THAT! I **TOLD** YOU I'D DO THE HEAVY WORK!

IT **NEVER** ENDS. ONLY THE FACES CHANGE.

DAD!

GRANDMA, I HAVE A HURT FINGER!

OH, MY!

AND IT HURTS REAL BAD, TOO!

HOW WOULD YOU LIKE A NICE APPLE, RUTHIE?

GEE, GRANDMA, YOU CAN DO BETTER'N THAT!

I'M OUT OF COOKIES, DEAR.

WHAT A WASTE!

HOW ABOUT A BRAN MUFFIN?

CRYSTAL, THE GLAMOROUS MOVIE STAR, BRUSHES BACK HER LOVELY LONG HAIR.

SHE IS TOO BEAUTIFUL FOR WORDS... OR EVEN SENTENCES.

DINNER IS READY!

JOSIE, HER DOWNSTAIRS MAID, CALLS HER TO DINNER.

RUTHIE, DID YOU HEAR ME?!

YES, MOM, I'LL BE THERE IN A MINUTE!

IS THAT YOUR BOOK, RUTHIE?

HAH-HAH! NO, GRANDPA, THIS BOOK IS NOT AT MY READING LEVEL!

OH... AND WHERE EXACTLY **IS** YOUR READING LEVEL?

ABOUT RIGHT HERE.

CLOSE YOUR MOUTH, NICK. IT'S AN EASTER BONNET RUTHIE MADE FOR ME.

I TOLD HER I COULDN'T WEAR IT ON EASTER, BUT I'D BE HAPPY TO WEAR IT ON SOME OTHER SPECIAL OCCASION.

OH.

WHAT'S THE SPECIAL OCCASION?

YOU'RE DOING THE DISHES.

HEE, HEE, HEE! HAH, HAH!

SAY IT AGAIN, DADDY, PLEASE?

COME ON, RUTHIE, YOU'RE BEING SILLY!

PLEASE, DAD, PLEASE!

OH, ALL RIGHT...

SQUEEGEE.

HAH! HEE, HEE, HO, HAH, HAH!

A KID AT MY SCHOOL HAS GREEN TEETH!

DID ANYBODY EVER DIE FROM SWALLOWING THIS STUFF?

MY GRANDMA'S TEETH SLEEP IN A GLASS AT NIGHT.

GUESS HOW MANY STEPS TO OUR UPSTAIRS?

WHAT'S THE WEATHER LIKE THERE?

RUTHIE!

WHATEVER POSSESSED YOU TO CALL THE 800 NUMBER ON THE TOOTHPASTE TUBE?!

JUST CURIOUS, I GUESS.

ONE DAY THE BEAUTIFUL PHEASANT GIRL WAS WALKING IN THE WOODS.

OOPS... I MEAN, **PEASANT** GIRL!

ONE DAY THE BEAUTIFUL PEASANT GIRL WAS PICKING BERRIES IN THE WOODS.

EXCUSE ME!

I SAID, EXCUSE ME!!!

A TALKING FROG!

NOT REALLY, I'M ACTUALLY A HANDSOME PRINCE!

BUT A CRANKY OLD WITCH CAST A SPELL ON ME, TURNING ME INTO A FROG!

IF YOU KISS ME, THOUGH, I WILL TURN BACK INTO A PRINCE AND MARRY YOU AND GIVE YOU LOADS OF NEAT STUFF!

THE BEAUTIFUL PEASANT GIRL THOUGHT ABOUT IT FOR ABOUT A MINUTE AND A HALF.

FORGET IT, FROG! I'M NOT KISSING ANYTHING THAT HAD **BUGS** FOR BREAKFAST!

THEN SHE SKIPPED BACK TO TOWN AND GOT HER REAL ESTATE LICENSE.

MY VERSIONS OF THESE STORIES MAKE A LOT MORE SENSE!

YEAH, AND I NOTICE THAT THEY TEND TO RAMBLE ON LONG PAST YOUR BEDTIME.

THE TOTAL COMES TO $2.35.

HMMM... TELL YOU WHAT...

LET'S CALL IT A DOLLAR EVEN.

LET'S CALL IT $2.35!

LADY, I DON'T THINK YOU'RE QUITE GETTING THE PICTURE HERE!

KID, WEREN'T YOU IN HERE YESTERDAY ASKING FOR A REFUND ON GREEN GUMDROPS?

OKAY, $1.50!

GEE, DINOSAURS WERE SO BIG WE COULD NEVER HAVE HAD ONE AS A PET... HUH, MOM?

THAT'S RIGHT, JOE.

I MEAN, IF A DINOSAUR FOLLOWED ME HOME, YOU'D SAY, "NO WAY!" RIGHT?

UH... RIGHT.

WELL, YOU'LL BE GLAD TO KNOW THAT SOMETHING MUCH **SMALLER** THAN A DINOSAUR IS RIGHT OUTSIDE!

WHAT?!

DON'T WORRY... JOE HAS THIS ALL FIGURED OUT!

JOE, WHERE'S THAT BIG OL' DOG YOU WAS MESSIN' WITH YESTERDAY?

HIS OWNER CAME AND GOT HIM.

HE WAS A ST. BERNARD DOG!

I KNOW, AND HE SLOBBERED A LOT.

THAT'S CUZ HE WAS **DRUNK!** THEM DOGS CARRY **BOOZE** AROUND THEIR NECKS!

JAMES, I GOTTA GO IN NOW.

AND IT PAINS MY LI'L HEART TO SEE 'EM IN THAT PITIFUL CONDITION!

YOUR HEART'S ON THE **OTHER** SIDE, JAMES.

One Big Happy

HEE, HEE, HEE!
RUTHIE, SHH!

WHAT'S THIS?!
HEE, HEE, HEE!

JOE and RUTHIE'S TOP TEN LIST OF THINGS **MOM** SAYS

10 DON'T TOUCH A THING ON YOUR WAY TO THE BATHROOM!

9 WHEN I SAY 7:00, I **MEAN** 7:00.

8 SPARE ME THE DRAMATICS.

7 CLOSE THE DOOR, PLEASE!

6 IN A MINUTE! I'M ON THE PHONE NOW!

5 CALM DOWN AND START OVER.

4 WHY DIDN'T YOU GO BEFORE YOU LEFT?!

3 JUST TRY A LITTLE. YOU DON'T HAVE TO EAT THE WHOLE THING.

2 I'M NOT YOUR MAID.

AND NOW, THE NUMBER ONE THING THAT MOM SAYS, AND OUR MOST FAVORITE!

1 I LOVE YOU.
WE LOVE YOU TOO, MOM!
HAPPY MOTHER'S DAY!

DAD, I FINISHED MY REPORT!

A Report on **CATS** by Joe (the GREAT) written by JOE drawn by JOE

The Ancient Egyptians liked cats so much they even had a cat goddess named Bastet.

The Chinese thought cats could talk when they got to be ten years old.

In the Middle Ages, people were cruel to cats because they hung around with witches. (The cats, I mean).

One time in England a cat ran away and when it came back 4 years later it was 45 inches long and weighed 30 lbs.

There are Alley Cats and Tom Cats and Fraidy Cats.

Siamese cats are the ones who got the girl dog in trouble in that cartoon movie.

Whenever a cat makes doody in my grandma's garden, she chases it, even in her bathrobe.

The End

IT'S TERRIFIC, JOE. I WOULDN'T CHANGE A THING, EXCEPT MAYBE THIS ONE LITTLE PART...

WHAT PART?!

ONE BIG HAPPY

LONG AGO, IN A REAL OLD COUNTRY NOBODY CARES ABOUT ANYMORE...

THERE ONCE LIVED THIS GUY NAMED MIDAS WHO WAS A KING OR SOMETHING.

HE WAS REAL RICH AND HAD A MUFFLER STORE, BUT HE WANTED TO BE RICHER.

SO HE MADE A DEAL WITH THE DEVIL OR A GENIE OR A WITCH OR SOMEBODY...

AND EVERYTHING HE TOUCHED TURNED TO GOLD!

IT WAS REAL NEAT AT FIRST.

BUT HE HAD TROUBLE WITH PERSONAL HYGIENE AND STUFF...

OUCH!

AND ACCIDENTALLY TURNED HIS DAUGHTER INTO A HOOD ORNAMENT.

THEN THERE WAS A BIG CAR CHASE AND EVERYBODY GOT KILLED IN THE END.

WOW, THAT'S SOME BOOK REPORT!

JOE, DID YOU EVEN **READ** THE BOOK?

WELL...I SORT OF SAW THE VIDEO, I THINK.

ONE BIG HAPPY

🎵 I'M GETTING MARRIED IN THE MORNING. DING DONG, THE WITCH IS DEAD... 🎵

UH... OR SOMETHING LIKE THAT!

I'M OFF TO VISIT MY BOYFRIEND...

IN MY PINK CORVETTE...

THAT CAN FLY!

WHEEEEEE!

DARLING!

DON'T "DARLING" ME, YOU JAILBIRD!

HERE YOU SIT ROTTING IN PRISON FOR BEATING UP A BANK MACHINE! I **WARNED** YOU ABOUT YOUR UGLY TEMPER!

WHY ARE YOU WEARING THAT DRESS?

I CAN'T WAIT FOR YOU, SO I'M MARRYING SOMEONE ELSE!

WHO?!

HIM! HE'S KIND OF WEIRD, BUT HE'S EASY TO BOSS AROUND!

GEE... PLAYING DOLLS SURE HAS CHANGED SINCE I WAS A GIRL!

OKAY, GRANDMA, START THE DINOSAUR STAMPEDE!

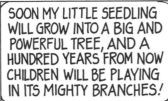

55

THE FIERCE STORM SMASHES THE SHIP AGAINST THE ROCKS.

EVERYBODY GETS DROWNED! WELL, **ALMOST** EVERYBODY.

CRYSTAL, THE BEAUTIFUL ADVENTURE GIRL, **FINDS HERSELF ON A** DESERTED ISLAND.

SHARKS AND ALLIGATORS SWIM IN THE DARK WATERS ALL AROUND.

BUT CRYSTAL IS FEARLESS. SHE KNOWS KARATE AND DID THE STAIRMASTER A LOT.

THE ONLY OTHER CREATURES ON THE ISLAND ARE A COUPLE OF STRANGE LITTLE SOCK PEOPLE.

HI! HOW YA DOIN'?

I BE OOBIE, AND THIS BE PITTIE

THEY ADMIRE AND LOOK UP TO CRYSTAL, MAINLY BECAUSE SHE'S A LOT TALLER THAN THEM.

OOO...SHE BE FAST!

OOKIE OOOK!

LIFE ON THE ISLAND IS HARD.

HEY!

SUDDENLY, A GIANT WEIRD-LOOKING BEAST APPEARS IN THE SURF!

RUTHIE, YOUR BEDTIME WAS **TWO HOURS** AGO!

A **BOSSY** BEAST!

WHAT DID YOU HAVE FOR LUNCH TODAY, RUTHIE?

PIZZA.

SPECIAL TOPPINGS?

NO, JUST CHEESE AND OLIVES.

BLACK OLIVES?

YES.

HOW ABOUT DESSERT? ICE CREAM SUNDAE.

CHOCOLATE SAUCE?

YES, AND A CHERRY.

MARASCHINO?

YOU'RE STILL ON THAT DIET, AREN'T YOU, GRANDPA?

HOW CAN YOU TELL?

GRANDPA, WHEN I DIE, WILL I GO TO HEAVEN OR TO YOU-KNOW-WHERE?

WELL, JOE, THAT'S PRETTY MUCH UP TO YOU, DON'T'CHA THINK?

I GUESS SO.

GRANDPA, DO YOU THINK GOD GRADES ON THE CURVE?

I SURE HOPE SO.

I SAW A REAL PROFESSIONAL POKER GAME ON TV!

IT WAS JUST LIKE OUR GAME, EXCEPT THEY DIDN'T GAB AS MUCH AS WE DO; AND THEY DIDN'T HAVE AS MANY WILD CARDS...

AND THEIR CHIPS WERE WORTH REAL MONEY...

OOOH! I'LL BE RIGHT BACK!

AND THEIR DEALER DIDN'T HAVE TO CHECK ON HER CHICKEN EVERY FEW MINUTES!

Panel 1:
HI, RUTHIE! WHAT'S UP?

MY TEACHER CHOSE **ME** TO TALK TO THE KINDERGARTEN KIDS!

Panel 2:
I'M GOING TO MAKE A SPEECH, TELLING THEM WHAT FIRST GRADE IS LIKE!

Panel 3:
UH-HUH...

Panel 4:
AND THE HELMET AND BAT?

IN CASE THERE'S TROUBLE!

Panel 5:
WHAT TO EXPECT IN FIRST GRADE, BY RUTHIE.

Welcome, Ruthie!

Panel 6:
FIRST GRADE IS BETTER THAN KINDERGARTEN BECAUSE OUR FIRST GRADE TEACHER, MISS CHOWDER, HAS A LOT OF PERSONAL PROBLEMS.

Panel 7:
THAT MEANS SHE'S LATE MOST MORNINGS, AND WE CAN FOOL AROUND TILL SHE COMES IN!

Panel 8:
RUTHIE... RUTHIE!

SHE SAYS IT'S CAR TROUBLE, BUT WE THINK HER BOYFRIEND, YOU KNOW, **DRINKS!**

Panel 9:
I RECEIVED AN INTERESTING PHONE CALL FROM YOUR SCHOOL PRINCIPAL TODAY!

UH-OH!

Panel 10:
IT SEEMS YOU TOLD THE KINDERGARTEN CLASS THAT YOUR TEACHER'S BOYFRIEND HAS A DRINKING PROBLEM!

YES, I DID!

Panel 11:
BECAUSE ONLY BY SHARING OTHER PEOPLE'S PROBLEMS CAN WE LEARN ABOUT NOT DOING BAD THINGS, AND WEIRD STUFF IS INTERESTING!

Panel 12:
RUTHIE, WHAT ARE YOU TALKING ABOUT?

RATINGS, MOM, BIG RATINGS.

ONCE UPON A TIME, IN A HOUSE BY THE SEA...

LIVED A LITTLE GIRL NAMED PEA POD.

ONE DAY LITTLE PEA POD WAS PLAYING IN HER MOTHER'S JEWELRY BOX...

SUDDENLY SHE DROPPED HER MOM'S GOLD LOCKET DOWN THE DRAIN.

OOPS!

PEA POD'S SISTER ASKED:

WHAT ARE YOU DOING?

NOTHING!

THE LIE BEGAN.

THEIR MOM ASKED:

PEA POD, HAVE YOU BEEN PLAYING IN MY JEWELRY BOX?

NO, MOMMA.

PEA POD'S LIE GREW.

THEIR DAD ASKED:

HON, WHERE'S YOUR GOLD LOCKET?

A MAN STOLE IT!

THE LIE GREW BIGGER.

WHAT MAN?

A BIG, UGLY GUY WITH A PURPLE PONYTAIL!

THE LIE GREW EVEN BIGGER!

SOON PEA POD'S LIE FILLED THE ENTIRE ROOM.

AND THE GUY HAD A BEARD!

LET'S CALL THE POLICE!

WELL, WHAT DO YOU THINK SO FAR?

COOL! THAT LIE COULD BE HER BODY-GUARD!

YEAH! IT COULD HELP CARRY IN THE GROCERIES AND STUFF!

AND THE MORAL OF THE STORY GOT SMALLER AND SMALLER...

One Big Happy

* SIGH *

ROSE?

YES?

UH... NOTHING.

WHAT IS IT, NICK? SOMETHING'S BOTHERING YOU.

YOU KNOW, SHAKESPEARE SAID, "YOU UNPACK YOUR LIFE WITH WORDS."

CHIPPED DISH?! I HAVE RIGHTS! I'M NOT TAKING THE BLAME FOR EVERYTHING!

AND WHAT GOOD IS SUMMER IF YOU HAVE TO WORK?! DUSTING CAN KILL YOU! THEY SAID SO ON TV!

AND DON'T THINK I FORGOT ABOUT THOSE STOLEN FRIES, **BIG BROTHER!**

GRRRR... MUMBLE, MUMBLE...

AND SOME PEOPLE ARE UNPACKED BEFORE THEIR LUGGAGE ARRIVES!

WHICH TWO COLORS, WHEN MIXED TOGETHER, PRODUCE ORANGE?

RUTHIE?

MR. WELLS

COLOR WHEEL

YELLOW AND BLUE!

NO, YELLOW AND BLUE MAKE GREEN.

GREEN IS A VERY NICE COLOR!

IF I CAN'T BE RIGHT, I'LL BE LOUD.'

EEYAH!

UH... HELLO, DO WE KNOW YOU?

DANG STRAIGHT! I AM THE KICKBOX KING! COOTIE KILLER, COYOTE JOE!

IT'S JAMES, GRANDPA! HE LIVES ON ASH STREET.

THANK GOODNESS, FOR A MINUTE THERE I THOUGHT HE WAS ONE OF **MY** GRANDCHILDREN.

HE POPS A LOT OF COUGH DROPS, YA KNOW?

MOM, DO YOU KNOW WHAT I REALLY, **REALLY** WANT? A LITTLE SISTER!

OH, THAT'S VERY SWEET, RUTHIE, BUT I CAN'T PROMISE YOU ONE ANYTIME IN THE NEAR FUTURE.

OH.

WELL, THEN, HOW ABOUT A COCKER SPANIEL THAT KNOWS HOW TO MAKE THE BED?

One Big Happy

HI, JOE. WHERE'S MOM?

MOM!

WHAT IS IT?! I'M IN HERE!

SHE'S IN THERE.

OH.

MOM, WILL YOU SIGN MY PAGICIAN?

PAGICIAN? DO YOU MEAN PETITION?

A BIG KID AT SCHOOL GAVE IT TO ME. I'M SUPPOSED TO GET ALL THE FIRST GRADERS TO SIGN IT.

"WE THE UNDERSIGNED DEMAND THAT THE SCHOOL CAFETERIA SERVE SODAS..."

RUTHIE, WHY SHOULD **I** SIGN IT? I'M NOT A FIRST GRADER!

MOM, A LOT OF FIRST GRADERS CAN'T WRITE THEIR NAMES! SO YOU CAN SIGN FOR THEM!

LET'S START WITH KRISTI. I DON'T KNOW HER LAST NAME, SO JUST PUT "SMITH" OR "BRUNOWSKI."

RUTHIE, IN THE FIRST PLACE, IT'S AGAINST THE LAW TO SIGN A NAME OTHER THAN YOUR OWN ON A PETITION...

AND, IN THE SECOND PLACE, I DON'T **WANT** THE SCHOOL CAFETERIA TO CARRY SODA POP!

BUT, MOM, WHAT AM I GOING TO DO? THE BIG KID SAID...

YOU'RE GOING TO DO THE RIGHT THING, AND YOU KNOW EXACTLY WHAT THAT IS!

YEAH... I GUESS SO.

GRANDPA, WILL YOU SIGN MY PAGICIAN?

66

RUTHIE, WHAT HAPPENED TO YOUR DOLL?!

OH, HER HEAD GOT STUCK IN THE CLOSET DOOR.

BUT YOU CONTINUE TO PLAY WITH HER?

SURE, GRANDMA! SHE STILL DRESSES UP AND GOES SHOPPING AND WORKS ON HER COMPUTER. SHE'S JUST LIKE SHE WAS BEFORE!

'CEPT NOW SHE HAS LOW SELF-ESTEEM.

I'M NOT SURPRISED!

LOOK, RUTHIE, HERE COMES KEVIN'S AUNT, THE SISTER!

THE WHAT?

GOOD ART BY RUTHIE

Only 5¢ Drawed while you wait!

YOU KNOW, THE NUN, LIKE IN *THE SOUND OF MUSIC!*

OH YEAH, *THE SOUND OF MUSIC!*

Only 5¢

HI, SISTER KATE!

HI, JOE! HI, RUTHIE!

GOOD HI!

Only 5¢ Drawed while you wait!

NO, THERE ARE NO NAZIS CHASING ME!

GOOD ART BY RUTHIE

Draw while you wait!

MOM, HOW DO YOU SPELL GNAT?

G-N-A-T.

WHAT ARE YOU WRITING, RUTHIE?

A BOOK! IT'S KIND OF LIKE ANOTHER FAMOUS BOOK....

BUT MY BOOK IS COMPLETELY DIFFERENT, WITH A DIFFERENT CHARACTER, SO IT'S REALLY VERY ORIGINAL!

"THE GNAT IN THE HAT."

Rick Detorie Productions *presents* **One Big Happy**

CAST
RUTHIE..............RUTHIE
RUTHIE..............JOE

RUTHIE, THE WORLD-FAMOUS ACTRESS, PREPARES FOR HER NEXT PERFORMANCE.

SHE CHECKS THE HOUSE.

BIG CROWD?

YEP.

RUTHIE KNOWS HER AUDIENCE.

IS GRANDPA STILL HERE?

YES.

HOW ABOUT AUNT JO?

YES.

SHE RUNS THROUGH HER LINES ONE LAST TIME.

SHE TAKES A DEEP BREATH...

AND MAKES HER GRAND ENTRANCE!

MOM, I CAN'T SLEEP. MY BAND-AID KEEPS COMING OFF!

RUTHIE, YOU SHOULD'VE BEEN ASLEEP HOURS AGO!

OH... SNACKS!

ANOTHER BRILLIANT PERFORMANCE!

RUTHIE, MRS. VAETH JUST CALLED. DID YOU FORGET TO WALK HER DOG TODAY?

OH, YEAH!

I DON'T FEEL LIKE WALKING ROWDY TODAY, DAD. I'LL CALL IN SICK!

RUTHIE, WE'VE DISCUSSED THIS BEFORE. YOU DON'T WORK FOR MRS. VAETH. YOU'RE SELF-EMPLOYED!

OH, YEAH, I FORGOT!

SELF-EMPLOYED PEOPLE DON'T GET SICK.

DAD, A KID AT THE PARK SAID HIS DAD COULD BEAT UP OUR DAD!

WELL, I HOPE YOU SET HIM STRAIGHT!

CAN WE SEE YOUR MUSCLE?

SURE! WELL?

MAYBE YOU COULD USE STEREOS!

STEROIDS!

RUTHIE, I DON'T KNOW IF THIS BUG IS A CRICKET OR A STINK BUG!

SMELL IT! IF IT'S A STINK BUG, IT WILL STINK!

SNIFF PYEEEW! IT SMELLS LIKE TUNA SALAD!

EEEW! IT MUST BE A STINK BUG!

JOE, HAVE YOU WASHED YOUR HANDS SINCE LUNCH?

RUTHIE, I NEED THE BLACK MARKER TO DRAW A MUSTACHE!

OKAY, JAMES, BUT MAKE IT QUICK, WILL YA?

I FINISHED MY DRAWING, AND I NEED TO SIGN MY NAME IN BLACK!

COME ON, JAMES, WHERE'S THAT MUSTACHE?

JAMES! YOU DREW A MUSTACHE ON YOURSELF WITH A MARKER?!

ARE YOU CRAZY? ARE YOU NUTS? WHAT'S THE MATTER WITH YOU?!

YOU WANT ME TO DRAW ONE ON YOU?

A MUSTACHE?! DON'T BE RIDICULOUS! OF COURSE NOT!

MAYBE A COUPLE OF EYEBROWS, THOUGH.

OKAY, HOLD STILL!

RUTHIE!

I COULDN'T HELP MYSELF, MOM!

SHE MADE ME DO IT, RUTHIE'S MOM!

GO WASH IT OFF RIGHT NOW, AND LET'S HOPE IT ISN'T PERMANENT INK!

WHAT IF IT IS?

THEN MAYBE YOU'LL BOTH HAVE TO GET JOBS AS PROFESSIONAL IMPERSONATORS.

AS JOAN CRAWFORD AND THE FRITO BANDITO!

WHO?

GROWN-UP STUFF.

AND SO, THE EVIL CLAW ROAMS THE STREETS AT NIGHT, SEARCHING OUT LITTLE CHILDREN WHO DON'T GO TO BED PROMPTLY AT THEIR BEDTIME.

OH, DADDY! THAT'S A DUMB STORY!

YOU THINK SO?

MY TURN! THIS IS RUTHIE'S BEDTIME STORY!

ONCE UPON A TIME, THERE WAS A BEAUTIFUL PRINCESS NAMED CIARA.

SHE LIVED IN THE CASTLE WITH HER FATHER THE KING, BUT WE'RE NOT SURE HE'S HER **REAL** FATHER, YOU KNOW?

BUT THE KING WASN'T HOME CUZ HE WAS AT THE BETTY FORD CLINIC, OR SOMEPLACE LIKE THAT.

AND CIARA'S BROTHER, PRINCE RIDGE, LIVED IN A CAVE WITH A LADY DRAGON WHO HAD AN EATING DISORDER.

SO THE ONLY ONE IN THE CASTLE WITH CIARA WAS HER DAUGHTER STACEY, WHO WAS ONLY ABOUT TWO YEARS YOUNGER THAN CIARA.

YOU HAVEN'T HEARD THE LAST OF ME, MOTHER!

ONE DAY A LADY APPEARED AT THE DOOR.

HEY, DON'T I KNOW YOU?

SHE LOOKED KIND OF FAMILIAR, MAYBE BECAUSE SHE HAD BEEN IN OTHER STORIES AND A FEW COMMERCIALS, BUT THOSE WEREN'T THE ONLY REASONS.

IT'S CUSTOM-MADE FOR BABY'S LEAKS!

WHAT DO YOU THINK SO FAR?

I THINK YOU WATCH ENTIRELY TOO MANY SOAP OPERAS WITH YOUR GRANDMOTHER!

ROSE, DO YOU KNOW MAISIE LEE WHO LIVES ON UNION AVENUE?

SURE: "CRAZY MAISIE."

SHE'S A NASTY, CANTANKEROUS OLD THING! EVERY TIME SHE RIDES THE BUS, SHE POKES THE OTHER PASSENGERS AND SHRIEKS, "GIMME THAT SEAT, YOU PEON!"

WELL, SHE DIED YESTERDAY.

OH, THAT POOR SOUL! ALL SHE WANTED OUT OF LIFE WAS A SEAT ON THE BUS.

THAT'S THE FINAL TOUCH!

TA-DAH!

IT'S TAKEN MOST OF THE SUMMER TO ASSEMBLE, BUT IT WAS WORTH IT!

A 1955 AUSTIN-HEALEY 100!

HOW ARE WE GONNA WRECK IT?

WHAT SEEMS TO BE THE PROBLEM?

THIS HERE FISH SWALLOWED BATMAN!

DR. RUTHIE'S MERGENCY ROOM

I SEE... WELL, WHICH ONE IS THE PATIENT?

OH!

DR. RUTHIE'S MERGENCY ROOM

UH...

DR. RUTHIE'S MERGENCY

LET ME PUT IT THIS WAY, WHICH ONE HAS INSURANCE?

DR. RUTHIE'S MERGENCY

MOM, WE SAW LADIES IN BIKINIS ON THE HIGHWAY!

THEY WERE WAXING CARS!

AN AUTO-DETAILING PLACE ON TAFT ROAD IS USING BIKINI-CLAD GIRLS TO WOO CUSTOMERS.

HUH! WHAT A SEXIST, DEGRADING, SLEAZY PRACTICE!

YEAH!

BUT THEY SURE MADE OUR CAR LOOK GREAT!

IT WAS LOVE. IT WAS PEACE. IT WAS THE WHOLE HAIGHT-ASHBURY THING!

YEAH, AND IT, LIKE, CULMINATED AT WOODSTOCK!

WHAT ARE THOSE MEN TALKING ABOUT, MOM?

THEY'RE REMINISCING ABOUT THE '60s.

OH, YEAH! GRANDPA AND MR. FOLEY DO THAT ALL THE TIME.

THEY DO?!

AND WHEN I WAS SIXTY-SIX, I DEVELOPED THIS ACHE IN MY SHOULDER!

YEP, MY BACK WENT OUT ON MY SIXTY-FIRST BIRTHDAY!

WHAT'S WRONG, RUTHIE?

I JUST SAID GOOD-BYE TO MELISSA.

SHE'S LEAVING TO GO VISIT HER AMMY!

HER AMMY? WHAT'S AN AMMY?

I DON'T KNOW. SHE SAID, "WE'RE GOING TO VISIT MY AMMY."

OH, MIAMI!

NO, MOM, HER AMMY!

OH, WHAT CUTE SHOES! WHERE DID YOU GET THEM?

THE STORE WITH THE CIRCLES ON THE FLOOR.

HENSHEY'S.

WHERE IS HENSHEY'S?

IT'S ON THE STREET WITH THE GIANT FAKE COW.

ELMHURST.

WHO ARE YOU, HER FATHER?

GRANDFATHER.

INTERPRETER.

MOM, THIS SOUP IS COLD!

IT'S **SUPPOSED** TO BE COLD.

NO WAY! SOUP IS **SUPPOSED** TO BE HOT!

LISTEN...

WHEN A MOTHER SLAVES ALL DAY OVER A HOT STOVE, HER CHILDREN ARE **SUPPOSED** TO GRATEFULLY AND POLITELY EAT WHAT SHE PUTS IN FRONT OF THEM.

IF THE STOVE WAS **HOT**, WHY IS THE SOUP **COLD**?

OH, ALL RIGHT, I'LL HEAT IT UP!

MINE, TOO!

MOM, I'M SCARED!

RUTHIE, WHAT ARE YOU AFRAID OF?

AN ELF GRANDPA TOLD ME ABOUT!

AN ELF?!

YEAH, IT BELONGS TO A GUY NAMED FEERIT!

GRANDPA SAID, "THE ONLY THING WE HAVE TO FEAR IS FEERIT'S ELF!"

RUTHIE...

TELL ME, ELLEN, DID YOU HAVE SECOND THOUGHTS ABOUT MOVING RIGHT NEXT DOOR TO YOUR IN-LAWS?

LET ME PUT IT THIS WAY...

THE FIRST TIME I MET MY MOTHER-IN-LAW, SHE WAS WASHING THE **OUTSIDE** OF HER HOUSE.

OH, DEAR!

YEAH, BUT WE MOVED IN ANYWAY.

I'LL PAY YOU A QUARTER TO DRAW WHATEVER YOU WANT.

GOOD ART BY RUTHIE

OKAY!

Only 5¢ Drawed while you wait

GOOD ART BY RUTHIE

Only 5¢

MAY I SEE THE QUARTER, PLEASE?

SURE! WHY?

INSPIRATION.

GOOD ART BY RUTHIE

Only 5¢

MOM, WILL YOU PLEASE PUSH ME?

RUTHIE, YOU CAN SWING YOURSELF!

NO, I CAN'T!

YES, YOU CAN. I KNOW YOU CAN!

I CAN'T DO IT!

YOU **CAN** DO IT!

IT'S ABOUT TIME SHE LEARNED THIS LESSON!

WHAT'S GOING ON?!

JOE, WE FOUND THIS BABY!

HE SEEMS TO HAVE WANDERED AWAY FROM HIS HOME!

MAYBE HE CAME FROM THE WILDERNESS!

YEAH, I SAW THIS MOVIE ABOUT A BABY WHO GOT LOST IN THE WILDERNESS AND FOUGHT A BEAR AND A BOBCAT AND RESCUED AN OLD TRAPPER WHO OWNED A LOG CABIN, AND, UH...

ON SECOND THOUGHT, MAYBE IT WAS A DOG!

A **DOG** OWNED A LOG CABIN?!

MOM, HOW ARE WE GONNA FIND THAT BABY'S HOME?!

WE'LL GO DOOR-TO-DOOR.

YOU KNOW, WE'D SAVE A LOT OF TIME IF WE HAD A MEGAPHONE! I ASKED YOU BEFORE IF WE COULD GET A MEGAPHONE, BUT NOOOO...

JOE, YOU'RE NOT GETTING A MEGAPHONE. WE DON'T **NEED** A MEGAPHONE, AND YOU KNOW WHY!

OH, YEAH.

WHOSE BABY IS THIS?!

BOY, THAT BABY'S MOM SURE WAS GLAD TO GET HIM BACK!

IT'S WEIRD THAT A BABY WOULD RUN AWAY FROM HOME LIKE THAT!

IT'S NOT SO UNUSUAL! ONCE, WHEN JOE WAS A BABY, AND MY BACK WAS TURNED, HE SLIPPED OUT AN OPEN DOOR!

I DID?!

WOW!

YES, AND YOU MADE IT TO THE END OF THE BLOCK WHERE YOU RAN INTO YOUR GRANDMOTHER RETURNING FROM THE MARKET.

JOE!

GEE, THAT MUST'VE BEEN SOME TRIP, HUH?

YOU MEAN JOE'S TRIP, OR THE **GUILT** TRIP YOUR GRANDMA TOOK ME ON?

BOTH!

UH... DID YOU SAY SOMETHING?

ONE DAY, WHILE EATING A GIANT BEAN, THE UGLY LITTLE PIG BOY HEARS A NOISE OUTSIDE.

HUH?

EEE! A GIANT GREEN MONSTER!

ERAW!

THE PIG BOY RUNS INTO THE KITCHEN.

PIG MOMMA, BIG MONSTER!

THE MONSTER CHASES THEM UPSTAIRS.

PIG DADDY, WHAT WE GONNA DO?!

TO THE ROOF!

THE PIG FAMILY HAULS THEIR BIG PIG BOTTOMS UP ONTO THE ROOF.

JOE, THEY ARE **NOT** PIG PEOPLE, AND GET THAT THING OUT OF MY DOLLHOUSE **NOW!**

BRIBBIT!

WHAT'S THAT, ELLEN?

IT'S A CLOTHES HAMPER THAT'S DIVIDED INTO SECTIONS.

SALE!

THIS TAG SAYS: "NOW THE ENTIRE FAMILY CAN PITCH IN AND HELP SORT THE LAUNDRY!"

HAH, HAH, HAH!

HEE, HEE, HEE, HEE!

MY FAMILY? USE A HAMPER?!

THIS IS A JOKE, RIGHT?

MOM, JOE CALLED ME A NAME!

I DID NOT!

HE SAID MY PHONE NUMBER IS 1·800· STINKY!

SO?

JOE, WE DON'T CALL EACH OTHER NAMES!

IT'S NOT A NAME, MOM!

HE HAS A POINT, ELLEN. IT'S NOT TECHNICALLY A NAME!

FRANK...

YOURS IS 1·800· MONKEY!

WHAT'CHA DOING, JOE?

WRITING A LETTER.

THE PLAYGROUND CLOSED DOWN BECAUSE A KID FELL OFF THE SLIDE AND HER PARENTS ARE SUING THE PLAYGROUND PEOPLE.

SO I'M WRITING A LETTER TO THE MOST AWESOME AND POWERFUL FORCE IN THE UNIVERSE.

YOU'RE WRITING A LETTER TO GOD?

NO, TO HIS LAWYER.

WHAT DID YOU FINALLY DECIDE TO DO FOR YOUR SCIENCE PROJECT?

THIS! I'M GOING TO OBSERVE THIS EGGPLANT UNTIL IT ROTS!

I SEE... AND WHEN IS THIS PROJECT DUE?

TOMORROW.

JOE, YOU EXPECT AN EGGPLANT TO ROT OVERNIGHT?

NOT ENOUGH TIME?

NAG IT! GRANDPA SAYS NAGGING WILL AGE ANYTHING!

THAT'S IT, I'M OUT OF CHIPS!

HERE, GRANDMA, TAKE SOME OF MINE!

NO, I WON'T ACCEPT CHARITY, RUTHIE! I'LL GET SOME REAL MONEY!

REAL MONEY?!

GRANDMA'S GOING TO PLAY WITH REAL MONEY?

WELL, REAL MONEY FOR HER, YOU KNOW.

I'LL SEE YOU WITH A COUPON FOR PAPER TOWELS, AND RAISE YOU ONE TEN-CENTS-OFF ON AIR FRESHENER.

JOE AND I ARE WATCHING A GOOD MOVIE, THE LAST OF THE MEXICANS.

THE WHAT?

IT'S ABOUT A BUNCH OF INDIANS AND SETTLERS FIGHTIN' AND STUFF!

MOHICANS, THE LAST OF THE MOHICANS.

MEXICANS ARE PEOPLE WHO ARE FROM MEXICO, A LARGE COUNTRY JUST SOUTH OF THE U.S.

OH.

WHERE'S MOHICO?

RING

SHHH! I CAN'T ANSWER THE PHONE NOW, I'M PLAYING HIDE 'N' SEEK!

Ruthie? Ruthie!

RUTHIE, PICK UP THE PHONE!

GEE, YOUR HOME LIFE IS INTERESTING, FRANK!

NEED A HAND, ELLEN?

SURE, ROSE!

YOU TWO ARE SO CUTE! AFTER ALL THESE YEARS, YOU'RE STILL HOLDING HANDS!

HOLDING HANDS?! IS THAT WHAT YOU CALL IT?

SURE! WHAT DO YOU CALL IT?

CHECKING HIS VITAL SIGNS.

WOW, MOM! YOU LOOK LIKE A BEAUTY PAGEANT LADY!

YEAH, LIKE A CONTESTANT!

THANK YOU! IT'S MY DREAM TO BE KIND TO CHILDREN AND THE ELDERLY, AND THEN BECOME A TV NEWS REPORTER...

AND INTERVIEW TRAGIC VICTIMS OF VIOLENT CRIME AND NATURAL DISASTERS WHILE WEARING EXPENSIVE DESIGNER OUTFITS AND ACRYLIC NAILS!

SHE SOUNDS LIKE A BEAUTY PAGEANT CONTESTANT, TOO!

FEELINGS... ♪

YEAH!

JAMES, I HEARD WHAT YOU TOLD MELISSA ABOUT ME, AND I DON'T LIKE IT ONE BIT!

LISTEN UP AND LISTEN GOOD! YOU'RE GOING TO CALL HER AND TELL HER YOU WERE WRONG! I'M NOT LIKE THAT.

AND YOU'RE GOING TO DO IT **NOW!** **UNDERSTAND?**

UH-HUH.

HELLO, MELISSA? RUTHIE IS **NOT** BOSSY.

WHO'S ON THE PHONE?

IT'S ANDY. HE WANTS TO BORROW $500 TO PAY OFF SOME OF HIS BILLS.

HELLO, ANDREW? IT'S YOUR MOTHER! WE'D BE DELIGHTED TO LEND YOU $500... AT 5% INTEREST.

THAT'S RIGHT, AND YOU MUST AGREE TO COME HERE REGULARLY FOR SUNDAY DINNER, AND GET YOURSELF A DECENT HAIRCUT!

OUR LOVE MAY BE UNCONDITIONAL, BUT NOT OUR CASH!

MOM, JOE PULLED MY HAIR!

DON'T PULL YOUR SISTER'S HAIR, JOE.

WAIT A MINUTE! YOU DON'T **KNOW** THAT I PULLED HER HAIR EXCEPT FOR HER SAY-SO!

IT'S NOT FAIR! NOBODY BELIEVES **ME!** YOU AUTOMATICALLY BLAME ME FOR EVERYTHING BEFORE YOU HEAR THE WHOLE STORY!

JOE, DID YOU PULL RUTHIE'S HAIR?

YES, OF COURSE, BUT THAT'S NOT THE POINT.

FOR THE HALLOWEEN PARTY, I'M GONNA BE A ZOMBIE CARRYING MY OWN BRAIN...

JOE...

INSTEAD OF DRESSING AS A GRISLY MONSTER, WHY NOT GO AS A HEROIC FIGURE THIS YEAR? MAYBE A PARAMEDIC OR A...

YEAH! OKAY, A PARAMEDIC!

A PARAMEDIC WHO GOT RUN OVER BY HIS OWN AMBULANCE! HE'S A ZOMBIE NOW, CARRYING HIS OWN BRAIN...

BOO!

YEAH, RIGHT, JOE.

LIKE, I'M REAL SCARED.

YOU'RE GONNA HAVE TO DO BETTER THAN THAT!

DO YOU HEAR ME?

PRESENTING... THE BEST HALLOWEEN COSTUMES ON THE BLOCK!

TA-DAH!

ONLY IN AMERICA!

HAH!

VERY GOOD!

THANK YOU VERY MUCH!

CUTE, FRANK, BUT DO THE KIDS EVEN KNOW WHO DON KING IS?

DON KING?!

I THOUGHT THEY WERE SUPPOSED TO BE YOUR AUNT DELIA!

THIS IS THE GREATEST COUNTRY IN THE WORLD!

ONE BIG HAPPY

RUTHIE, TIME TO GET UP!

DID YOU HEAR ME?

NO!

I DON'T **WANT** TO GET UP AND GO TO SCHOOL! IT'S NOT FAIR!

LIFE'S NOT FAIR, RUTHIE. THERE ARE LOTS OF THINGS I DON'T WANT TO DO, EITHER, BUT I DO THEM BECAUSE I HAVE TO.

I DON'T WANT TO GET OUT OF BED ON COLD MORNINGS.

I DON'T WANT TO HAVE MY TEETH CLEANED.

IT RAINED SO HARD, FRED'S CAR LEAKED LIKE CRAZY, ABOUT THREE INCHES OF WATER ON THE FLOOR OF THE PASSENGER SIDE. YOUR KIDS GO TO PUBLIC SCHOOL, DON'T THEY? MY SISTER... R KIDS TO A PRIVATE SCHOOL. THEY DO AE... MORNING BEFORE THE

I DON'T WANT TO BE COMPOSED AND SENSIBLE ALL THE TIME.

SHUT UP, YOU LITTLE MONSTER!

TREVOR, WE DON'T USE THAT KIND OF LANGUAGE HERE.

I DON'T WANT TO CLEAN THAT GUNKY STUFF OFF THE KETCHUP BOTTLE.

I DON'T WANT TO COOK FOOD THAT'S NOT EATEN.

JUST HAVE A COUPLE OF BITES!

I DON'T WANT TO SOUND EXACTLY LIKE MY MOTHER.

LIFE'S NOT FAIR, ELLEN. THERE ARE LOTS OF THINGS I DON'T WANT TO DO...

OH, ALL RIGHT, I GET IT... EVERYTHING BUT THAT LAST PART!

RUTHIE, WHEN ARE YOUR GLAMOUR GIRL DOLL AND SOLDIER DOLL GETTING MARRIED?

PROBABLY NEVER, GRANDMA!

G.I. JAKE DOESN'T WANT TO GET MARRIED! HE SAYS THAT MARRIAGE IS LIKE TAKING A BATH...

IT'S NOT SO HOT ONCE YOU GET USED TO IT!

WHERE DID YOU HEAR THAT? YOUR GRANDFATHER?

UH... I'M NOT SUPPOSED TO SAY!

I WANTED TO BE A DOCTOR WHEN I GROW UP, BUT NOW I DON'T THINK I CAN.

WHY NOT?

RUTHIE, YOU'RE BRIGHT; YOU CARE ABOUT PEOPLE; AND IF YOU SET YOUR MIND TO SOMETHING, THERE'S **NOTHING** YOU CAN'T DO!

WHAT MAKES YOU THINK YOU CAN'T BECOME A DOCTOR?

I CAN'T SAY MERMOMETER.

THERMOMETER?

MERMOMETER.

DAD, READ THE STORY ABOUT THE NAKED BASEBALL PLAYER!

NAKED BASEBALL PLAYER?

WELL, NOT A PLAYER... THE REFEREE, ACTUALLY!

YOU MEAN THE **UMPIRE**?

YEAH, THE ONE WITH NO CLOTHES!

NO CLOTHES?

THE EMPEROR'S NEW CLOTHES?

YEAH, **THAT'S** THE STORY!

ONE BIG Happy

JOE, YOU DROPPED SOMETHING!

IT'S A LIST, A LIST OF... AWWWW....

10 Good Things About My Family
by Joe (*THE GREATEST*)!!!

1. NONE OF US EVER GOT KILLED IN AN AVALANCHE.

2. MY MOM IS BEAUTIFUL AND MY DAD IS BRAVE.

YOU WANT ME TO PUT MY HAND IN THE POCKET?

YES, AND TELL ME IF WHAT YOU FEEL IS ALIVE!

3. MY PESKY SISTER DOESN'T KNOW WHERE I HIDE MY SECRET STUFF.

4. WE LIVE REAL CLOSE TO A VIDEO STORE.

YES!

VIDEOS VIDEOS VIDEOS

5. WE ALL LOVE EACH OTHER (EVEN THE ONES WE CAN'T STAND).

6. MY PARENTS DON'T TORTURE ME *TOO* OFTEN.

JOE, GIVE AUNT CONNIE A BIG KISS!

7. WE HAVE MORE THAN ONE BATHROOM.

I'M IN HERE! USE THE ONE DOWNSTAIRS!

8. MY GRANDPA GIVES ME MONEY SOMETIMES FOR *NO REASON.*

DON'T TELL YOUR GRANDMA, OKAY?

9. WE LEARN A LOT OF IMPORTANT THINGS FROM OUR ELDSTERS.

DOES A FLUSH BEAT A STRAIGHT?

10. WE'RE NOT THE SIMPSONS.